Create beautiful, lifelike artwork
that is uniquely yours.

The thrill of fresh colors on crisp paper awaits!

Select your palette and color over the gray, letting the depth of shading guide your choices. Optimize your coloring experience with these simple tips:

1. Color over the areas with the heaviest gray shading, using your darkest colors.

2. Color over the areas with the lightest gray shading, using your palest colors.

3. Use your medium colors to seamlessly blend light and dark.

Watch as the beauty of nature emerges from the grayscale!

And remember, you're the colorist. The magic happens when you allow the image to guide your process. It's okay to flip the steps. If you prefer to complete small sections at a time, go for it!

Get ready. Explore grayscale coloring tips and ideas for different coloring mediums. **Get inspired.** View tutorial videos and explore the coloring gallery. **Get noticed.** Upload your completed images to the gallery.

Beautiful
N A T U R E

A COLORING BOOK OF FLOWERS, PLANTS AND LANDSCAPES

Huelish
www.huelish.com

Cataloguing data available from Library and Archives Canada

ISBN 978-0-9948623-2-7 (paperback)

Book design by Elisa Gutiérrez
Cover art by Nicole Stocker

Photographs sourced from Allison Camille Tucker
(www.thecoloringgarden.com), Vanessa Courtney Bingham,
Vani Kurup Photography, Pixabay and Unsplash

FSC
www.fsc.org
MIX
Paper from
responsible sources
FSC® C016245

Printed and bound in Canada by
Friesens on FSC certified paper
which ensures that products come
from responsibly managed forests.

16 17 18 19 20   5 4 3 2 1

NICOLE STOCKER

NATURE

A COLORING BOOK OF FLOWERS, PLANTS AND LANDSCAPES

Color over the gray to bring your image to life

HUELISH

*N*ature calls to us from the time we are children. When a child first sits down to draw, trees, flowers, the sky and sun naturally emerge. Nature inspires the imagination and calms the soul. *Beautiful Creatures* re-awakened the joy of coloring, and now *Beautiful Nature* invites you to return to the page. Immerse yourself in the solitude of an arid desert, turn the page and take shelter in the stillness of an ancient forest. From wide-sweeping landscapes to the most delicate botanicals, *Beautiful Nature* harnesses the restorative power of the natural world.

Simply color over the gray, matching light and dark tones to reveal lifelike shading. Saturate the grayscale with heavy color, use the lightest of touches or simply let it be. Flood the page with vibrant brights or allow a softer color palette to emerge. As the colorist, you're free to immerse yourself in the space between black and white, and explore the many shades of your imagination.

Printed on acid-free, archival quality paper, perforated for framing, each piece offers an opportunity to explore your inner artist. Use your colors to breathe life into the grayscale, and lose yourself in the process. Whether your happy place is toes buried in the sand, nose-deep in a bloom or on a mountain top, *Beautiful Nature* can take you there, if only for a moment.

Nicole Stocker

Enjoy!

ARTWORK

by

COMPLETED ON

ARTWORK
by

COMPLETED ON

ARTWORK

by

COMPLETED ON

ARTWORK
by

COMPLETED ON

ARTWORK

by

COMPLETED ON

ARTWORK
by

COMPLETED ON

ARTWORK *by*

COMPLETED ON

ARTWORK
by

COMPLETED ON

ARTWORK

by

COMPLETED ON

ARTWORK

by

COMPLETED ON

ARTWORK
by

COMPLETED ON

ARTWORK
by

COMPLETED ON

ARTWORK

by

COMPLETED ON

ARTWORK by

COMPLETED ON

ARTWORK
by

COMPLETED ON

ARTWORK
by

COMPLETED ON

ARTWORK
by

COMPLETED ON

ARTWORK
by

COMPLETED ON

ARTWORK *by*

COMPLETED ON

ARTWORK
by

COMPLETED ON

ARTWORK
by

COMPLETED ON

ARTWORK
by

COMPLETED ON

ARTWORK
by

COMPLETED ON

ARTWORK
by

COMPLETED ON

ARTWORK

by

COMPLETED ON

ARTWORK

by

COMPLETED ON

ARTWORK *by*

COMPLETED ON

ARTWORK *by*

COMPLETED ON

ARTWORK by

COMPLETED ON

ARTWORK
by

COMPLETED ON

ARTWORK
by

COMPLETED ON

ARTWORK
by

COMPLETED ON

ARTWORK
by

COMPLETED ON

ARTWORK

by

COMPLETED ON

ARTWORK
by

COMPLETED ON

ARTWORK

by

COMPLETED ON

ARTWORK

by

COMPLETED ON

ARTWORK

by

COMPLETED ON

ARTWORK

by

COMPLETED ON

ARTWORK

by.

COMPLETED ON

ARTWORK

by

COMPLETED ON

ARTWORK
by

COMPLETED ON

ARTWORK
by

COMPLETED ON

ARTWORK

by

COMPLETED ON

ARTWORK
by

COMPLETED ON

ARTWORK
by

COMPLETED ON

ARTWORK
by

COMPLETED ON

As a young girl, Nicole was enchanted by a black and white photograph hanging in her parents' summer cabin, wishing she could bring it to life with color. An artist at heart, Nicole imagined a collection of coloring books filled with inspiring, carefully curated photographs. Following the beloved *Beautiful Creatures*, *Beautiful Nature* is the second in her series of elegant grayscale coloring books. A mother of two young children, Nicole treasures any moment to lose herself in color and creation in her Vancouver home.

Share your artwork. See what others are creating.

HUELISH

www.huelish.com

@huelish

Thank you for taking part in this coloring adventure.
Until the next one . . .

Nicole Stocker